Lucille Warner and Ann Reit

SCHOLASTIC INC.
New York Toronto London Auckland Sydney

ISBN 0-590-31723-7

19 18 17 16 15 8 9/9 0 1 2/0

Printed in the U.S.A. 01

WHO am I?
QUIZ BOOK

For Julie

Contents

I The Inside Me **1**
Am I an Extrovert or an Introvert?
Am I Confident?
Am I a Daydreamer?
Am I Timid?

II The Outside Me **17**
Am I Sociable?
Am I a Leader or a Follower?
Do I Make the Most of My Looks?
Am I Conventional or Unconventional?

III What Are My Talents? **31**
Am I Musical?
Am I Visual?
Am I Verbal?
Am I Mechanical?
Am I Athletic?

IV How Do I Deal with Family and Friends? 47

Parents?!?
Am I a Good Friend?
How Do I Get Along with My Brother or Sister?

V How Do I Act with the Opposite Sex? 61

Am I Relaxed on a Date?
Am I the Jealous Type?
Am I as Considerate as Possible?

VI How Do I See the World and How Do I See Myself Fitting into It? .. 73

Do I Keep Well Informed of Current Events?
Do I Have a Sense of Community Responsibility?
Can I Change the World?
Where in the World Will I Live?
What in the World Will I Do?

—— I ——

The Inside Me

The Inside You is the true you. It is the you who is all alone at night, thinking about the things that have happened during the day. The Inside You tells you the things you want and wish for that you never tell anybody else. It is also the you that knows what you don't like and what frightens you. Sometimes the Inside You embarrasses you or makes you blush with excitement, and sometimes the Inside You makes you dare to do something you've never done before.

No one knows your Inside You the way you do. And no one has to, either. It is all yours to keep as private as you want it to be. Sometimes, though, it can feel good to share your Inside You with someone special. Confiding in good friends and their confiding in you can make you feel happy and very close to one another.

But mostly, becoming aware of the Inside You helps *you*. It is probably one of the best ways to learn about the things that are most important to you.

Am I an Extrovert or an Introvert?

An extrovert is someone who is especially social and seems to enjoy being around people most of the time. An introvert is someone who prefers to keep to him- or herself.

1. I would find it more fun to:
   a) have a hamburger with a good friend.
   b) go to a party or club.

2. The sports I like best are (*mark the answer that includes most of the sports you enjoy*):
   a) basketball, volleyball, field hockey, football, softball.
   b) skiing, bicycle riding, running, swimming.

3. If I knew the answer to a question my teacher asked and no one else seemed to, I would:
   a) raise my hand and answer the question.
   b) not raise my hand.

4. In the last year I have made:
   a) more than 3 new friends.
   b) less than 3 new friends.

5. The people I admire most are:
   a) happiest and most comfortable in groups.
   b) private, quiet people who would rather be with one friend.

6. I would rather:
   a) go for a walk in the woods alone.
   b) go to a football game.

7. I would *dislike* most:
   a) waiting in a crowded bus station for a friend's arrival.
   b) waiting alone in my house for a friend to arrive.

8. When I am asked questions that I know the answers to, I:
   a) give short, simple answers.
   b) give answers with long explanations.

9. In group activities I am a:
   a) leader.
   b) follower.

10. If my class were divided into two groups, with half the class the most outgoing kids and the other half the least outgoing, which half would I be in?
    a) the most outgoing.
    b) the least outgoing.

SCORING: Total up your score by referring to this chart; then read below for an interpretation of your score.

	A	B
1.	0	5
2.	5	0
3.	5	0
4.	5	0
5.	0	5
6.	0	5
7.	0	5
8.	0	5
9.	5	0
10.	5	0

If your score falls between 5–15, it means that you are clearly more of an introvert than you are an extrovert. You probably prefer socializing in small rather than large groups. You may want to try exposing yourself to larger groups or maybe participate in a sport like volleyball, which requires group cooperation. That way you'll meet more people, which might be good to do.

If your score is between 20–30, you are in the middle range. Your personality incorporates a little of both the extrovert and the introvert. Being closer to one end of the scale indicates that you are more one way than the other. But generally, your score suggests that you are someone whose personality shifts comfortably with your mood and changing circumstances.

If your score is between 35–50, you are definitely more of an extrovert than an introvert. You enjoy being around people and participating in activities that require teamwork. You speak your mind and sometimes more. You might want to practice a little "introversion" once in a while.

Am I Confident?

To be confident means to believe in yourself and your capacity to do things well. Are you confident?

1. Before a test you have studied for, you:
   a) are afraid you can't and won't remember anything.
   b) hope that you're prepared and just want to get it over with.
   c) go around asking friends how much they studied.

2. When shopping for clothes, you:
   a) are reluctant to make a hasty decision, thinking that at another store they might have the same thing cheaper or something which you'll like better.
   b) quickly spot things you like and buy them.
   c) go home empty-handed because nothing seems right.

3. When you're at a restaurant, you:
   a) always order pretty much the same thing.

b) study the menu and then order what sounds good to you.
c) wait to hear what other people are ordering and, based on that, make your own decision.

4. Would you say your friends in general are:
   a) jealous of you and the things you are able to do?
   b) the kind of people you wish you could be?
   c) different individuals with their own strengths and weaknesses?

5. What do you think are the realistic chances of achieving what deep in your heart you want to do when you are an adult?
   a) 10–30%.
   b) 30–70%.
   c) 70–100%.

SCORING: Figure out your score by totaling the amount of points shown for each answer you chose. Read on for an interpretation.

	A	B	C
1.	1	3	2
2.	1	3	2
3.	1	3	2
4.	2	1	3
5.	1	2	3

If your score is between 12–15, you're confident — which probably doesn't come as much of a surprise to you. You are sure of who you are.

A score between 8–11 means you know what it feels like to be confident and also what it's like not to be. That's normal. You probably find that certain people and certain situations make you feel more confident than others.

If your score is between 5–7, you're a little low on the confidence scale. Don't worry; everybody has down periods when nothing good seems possible. Many teenagers feel that way a lot of the time. And why not? It's hard to believe in yourself at a time when you are changing so fast you can hardly keep up with it. As you come to know yourself better you'll learn to like yourself better, too.

Am I a Daydreamer?

Daydreamers are people who spend a good deal of their time absorbed in fantasy. Everyone daydreams; some people just do it more than others. How much do you daydream? How much does your daydreaming interfere with your everyday life?

1. Do you sometimes find yourself reading over passages in books that you have read at least once already and that weren't especially difficult to begin with?
   Yes No

2. In school do you gaze out the window looking at nothing in particular and dream that you're someplace altogether different?
   Yes No

3. Do you sometimes forget people's names almost as soon as they've been introduced to you?
   Yes No

4. Have you ever eaten a meal without realizing what it was you were putting in your mouth?
   Yes No

5. Do people frequently accuse you of forgetting something they told you earlier?
   Yes No

6. Are you accident-prone?
   Yes No

7. Do you often find yourself wishing that you were someplace else?
   Yes No

SCORING:

5–7 yes answers: You're a heavy day-dreamer lately. That can mean a lot of things. When people are bored they tend to daydream. Maybe you're unhappy doing what you're doing and daydreaming is your way of thinking about a time and place where you might be happier. It can also be a way of figuring out things, and at your age there's a lot to figure out.

Don't try to stop daydreaming — just watch out where you do it. Class isn't the best place; neither is crossing the street! Don't let it interfere with *living* your life.

3–4 yes answers: You do your share of daydreaming but not to the exclusion of other activities. Daydreaming can be fun and, in the right context, useful. Some writers and artists say they get their best ideas from daydreams.

1–2 yes answers: It seems as though you don't daydream much. If that's true you must be spending your time doing something else. Maybe you read a lot or squeeze in your homework whenever you find a free moment. Daydreaming can be relaxing. You may want to set aside a little time for it, if for no other reason than to see where your mind wanders.

Am I Timid?

To be timid means to be shy. Someone who is very timid is so self-conscious among other people that he or she tends to withdraw rather than reach out. Everybody's timid in some situations. When are you most timid?

1. When I'm with a new group of people in which I don't know anyone, I:
   a) circulate and introduce myself to those who seem interesting.
   b) wait for someone to approach me first.
   c) feel uneasy and try to avoid having to talk to anyone.

2. When my teachers ask for volunteers to answer questions, I raise my hand:
   a) never or very rarely.
   b) only every once in a while.
   c) pretty regularly.

3. When someone of the opposite sex tries to talk to me, I get embarrassed and:
   a) after a while begin to feel more comfortable.
   b) blush, my palms get sweaty, and sometimes I can hardly talk.
   c) make up an excuse to go away.

4. The longest I have gone without talking is:
   a) an hour or less.
   b) a few hours.
   c) a day or more.

5. If I was in a restaurant and was served something other than what I ordered, I would:
   a) be disappointed but settle for whatever I got.
   b) tell the waiter that I was given the wrong order and ask him to bring me what I wanted.
   c) eat what I got but say something about it when the waiter brings the check.

SCORING: Total the amount of points shown for each answer you chose.

	A	B	C
1.	5	10	15
2.	15	10	5
3.	5	15	10
4.	5	10	15
5.	15	5	10

A score between 60–75 indicates that difficult, pressured situations can make you feel shy and sometimes withdrawn. You are probably most comfortable when the least amount of attention is on you. Unfortunately, the situations that make you uneasy can't be completely avoided. Try absorbing yourself in whatever you're doing or thinking. You'll find that the more involved you are the less you'll worry about what others might be thinking about you.

40–55: You're not unfamiliar with timidity but you're not handicapped by it either. If you find that you're only timid in specific situations, try to understand why.

If your score is 25–35 you don't feel timid most of the time. That doesn't mean you never get nervous or self-conscious. You probably do as much as anyone else. You just deal with it well.

—— II ——

The Outside Me

Just as the Inside You is the way you feel and think of yourself, the Outside You is the way you behave and present yourself.

The Outside You is the you that your friends and acquaintances know. It is the person you are at school, during team practice, at an after-school job, or at a party. The way you act among other people, the way you speak and move, and the way you look are all aspects of the Outside You. While to you they're all just parts of the way you are, these more obvious qualities of yours are the first things others notice.

Am I Sociable?

Being sociable means being friendly. It means being at ease among other people and behaving in a likeable and acceptable manner. Being sociable also means being able to have a good time. Are you sociable?

Which of these choices describes you?

1. I would prefer most to:
   a) watch a favorite movie on TV alone in my bedroom.
   b) hang out with a bunch of friends and shoot the breeze.
   c) organize and throw a party.

2. When I find myself with an extra hour of free time I like to:
   a) take a stroll and daydream.
   b) find a friend to pass the time with.
   c) squeeze in a quick game of ball.

3. I think parties are:
   a) fun.
   b) interesting.
   c) a drag.

4. Just today I've talked to:
   a) less than 5 people.
   b) at least 10 people.
   c) over 15 people.

5. Away from home I like to:
   a) keep to myself and mind my own business.
   b) look around and observe people in relationship to one another.
   c) meet and talk with people who seem interesting.

SCORING: Total the number of points shown for each answer you chose.

	A	B	C
1.	5	10	15
2.	5	10	15
3.	15	10	5
4.	5	10	15
5.	5	10	15

A score of **25–40** suggests that today at least you don't feel too sociable. That's okay; not everyone does all of the time. It is possible, however, to protect your privacy and still reach out to other people. You'll probably find that the people you meet are also looking to make new friends.

A score of **45–55** indicates that you're a little bit unsure of yourself in social situations. You know what? Even the coolest person in school isn't always comfortable. The trick is to know how to hide the discomfort. Take the risk and meet someone new today.

If you scored between **60–75** you like people and they like you. Have fun but be careful; don't forget about yourself. Sometimes a couple of hours alone is a good thing, too.

Am I a Leader or a Follower?

A leader is someone who knows how to take command of a group of people. A leader is also someone who likes to organize group activities. A follower, on the other hand, is someone who prefers to be led. Without followers there would be no leaders in the world. One cannot exist without the other. Everybody has a little of both the leader and the follower in them. Usually, though, one quality is more dominant. Are you more of a leader than you are a follower?

1. When you're with a group of people who can't decide what to do, are you, generally, the one to make a suggestion?
   Yes No

2. Do you like to pull pranks?
   Yes No

3. Have you ever organized a surprise party?
   Yes No

4. Would your friends say you were persuasive?
   Yes No

5. When your teacher asks for volunteers, do you usually raise your hand?
   Yes No

6. Do you feel that you have a strong influence on your friends?
   Yes No

7. Would people say you were a trendsetter?
   Yes No

8. Of the last 6 movies you've seen, have 3 or more been *your* first choice?
   Yes No

SCORING:

1–3 yes answers: You think of yourself as more of a follower than a leader. You don't stick your neck out but prefer to check out the situation from afar.

4–6 yes answers: You've had experience being a leader and also being a follower. You probably realize that some situations call for you to be more aggressive than others. At other times you're probably more comfortable not being in the foreground.

7–8 yes answers: You see yourself in leadership roles among your friends and in various situations. Leaders are often very respected and depended upon but they may also be resented. Be careful not to be too bossy.

Do I Make the Most of My Looks?

As hard as it may be to believe, good looks have more to do with how people feel about themselves than they have to do with inheriting Uncle Charlie's perfect nose. Do you think you're as pretty or handsome as you could be? Have you been working on it?

1. Are you your perfect or preferred weight?
   Yes No

2. Do you take care of your clothes to make sure they are clean and pressed at all times?
   Yes No

3. Do people have to remind you that you need a haircut?
   Yes No

4. Do you go to school feeling grungy at times?
   Yes No

5. Do you ever put off washing your hair because you feel lazy?
   Yes No

6. Do you wear clothes that are cut and styled in a way that is most flattering to you?
   Yes No

7. If you have problems with your skin, are you following an effective treatment program?
   Yes No

8. Do you maintain a good, healthy diet?
   Yes No

9. Do you get regular exercise?
   Yes   No

10. Do you get enough sleep?
    Yes   No

SCORING: Total the number of points shown for each answer you chose.

	Yes	No
1.	10	0
2.	10	0
3.	10	0
4.	0	10
5.	0	10
6.	0	10
7.	10	0
8.	10	0
9.	10	0
10.	10	0

A score of 0–30 means you're not taking care of yourself. You'd be surprised how much better you'd look if you took time to tend to yourself. Not only will people compliment you but you'll feel better, too.

35–70 means you're being a little bit careless. Looking good not only means you're feeling good; it can also *make* you feel good. Take a good look at yourself in the mirror. What could use improving? What are your better features? Play them up.

75–100 means you know the importance of keeping yourself looking and feeling good. You also know that looking good requires effort. Keep up the regime; it's getting good results.

Am I Conventional or Unconventional?

An unconventional person is someone who is original. Some people are unconventional thinkers, other people are unconventional dressers. However, because no two people are alike, everybody is unique in some way or another. In which areas are you the most original? What is it about you that makes you stand out in the crowd?

1. The way I dress is:
   a) the way most young people dress in my town.
   b) is halfway between how my parents like me to look and how the kids dress at school.
   c) is unusual and a reflection of my unique personality.

2. I think that the pop records that are at the top of the charts are:
   a) cool.
   b) not always the best music around.
   c) I don't keep up with the charts.

3. When I cook for myself or friends, I:
   a) try to keep it simple, making something like hamburgers that don't call for too much work.
   b) like to try out new recipes.
   c) like to improvise, making up my own recipes.

4. When I go to the movies I:
   a) don't care what's playing; it's just fun to go.

b) like to see what's most popular.
c) usually choose pictures that seem interesting to me from the previews or newspaper reviews.

5. I dance:
   a) whatever's current.
   b) freestyle.
   c) as inconspicuously as I can.

SCORING:

	A	B	C
1.	10	5	15
2.	5	10	15
3.	5	10	15
4.	10	5	15
5.	5	15	10

A score of 25–40 suggests that for now at least you're happy to keep pace with others you age. You may not be very unconventional in public, but when you're alone you know that there is no one else in the world like you.

A score of 45–55 means you're unconventional without making too many waves.

A score of 60–75 suggests that you're someone with strong ideas of your own and you're not going to be swayed by prevailing trends. Watch out that you're not doing things just to be different.

—— III ——

What Are My Talents?

A talent is a person's natural ability to do something especially well. Some people are talented in music, other people are talented in art. Some people have a special talent for athletics, while others have talent in mechanical abilities. A person can be talented in languages and also the sciences.

There are many things that contribute to making people talented. Sometimes people in the same family have the same talents. A musician father, for instance, may have a musical child. Talents can be inherited by one member of a family from another, but they can also be developed. Children also can have talents all their own and very different from the talents of the other members of their family.

The tough things about a talent are uncovering it in the first place and then making some positive use of it. Do you know what areas you're most talented in? What are you doing about it?

Am I Musical?

1. Do you ever find certain pieces of music reminding you of certain times or experiences in your life?
   a) often   b) rarely   c) not really

2. When you watch a movie, do you:
   a) ignore the music and just follow the plot?
   b) notice the music and often appreciate how appropriate it is to the mood of the movie?
   c) feel as moved by the music as you are by the story?

3. Are there certain songs you like to play or hear because they express the way you are feeling?
   a) often   b) sometimes   c) rarely

4. If you listen to the radio, do you:
   a) mostly stay tuned in to your favorite music station?
   b) frequently change stations until you find a tune that pleases you?

c) keep it turned on for background music but don't really concentrate on what's playing?

5. Does some music make you feel like dancing or moving to the beat?
   a) often b) sometimes c) rarely

6. What does music mean to you?
   a) entertainment.
   b) expression.
   c) playing an instrument.

7. If you *don't* play an instrument, do you:
   a) often wish you did and sometimes even dream about playing one?
   b) feel lucky because that way you don't have to practice?
   c) not think about it one way or the other?

8. If you *do* play an instrument, do you:
   a) feel it's a chore, something you do because your parents make you?
   b) accept it as part of your daily routine?

c) get pleasure out of getting better and better at it?

SCORING:

	A	B	C
1.	15	10	5
2.	5	10	15
3.	15	10	5
4.	10	15	5
5.	15	10	5
6.	5	15	10
7.	5	10	15
8.	5	10	15

80–105: You love music and it evokes all sorts of feelings in you. If you play an instrument you probably are beginning to find out just how talented you are. If you don't play an instrument, maybe you should take up one. You obviously have the ability to derive a lot of pleasure from music.

55–75: Music moves you, but it may not inspire you. Become a cultivated listener.

You'll find your ear becoming more and more finely tuned to some of the more subtle qualities in music. You may not want to devote your life to music, but you appreciate it enough to know that you wouldn't want to be without it either.

35–50: Music is not your thing, or, at least, so far it's not. One day you may be surprised to find yourself really touched by a particular piece of music. If you're curious to know what you may be missing, ask a music lover you know to play some of his or her favorite records and tell you why they are favorites. Sometimes enthusiasm for music can be catching.

Am I Visual?

1. When you walk along the street do you:
   a) look straight ahead or at the ground?
   b) look around you at the people and places you're passing?

2. You have to buy a looseleaf notebook and you have a choice of one for $2.75 and a better-looking one for $3.75. You would:
   a) spend the extra dollar for the one that looks better.
   b) buy the cheaper one.

3. Have you ever looked at something and thought, "That would make a great picture"?
   a) never b) sometimes

4. You have a choice of wearing blue or black socks. The blue ones are a better match to what you are wearing but are dirty. You would:
   a) wash the blue ones and wear them
   b) wears the black ones.

5. Do you doodle?
   a) rarely b) often

6. Have you ever visualized the way you would like a place of your own to look?
   a) yes b) no

7. You and a bunch of friends buy some takeout food, and when you finally get home you are all so hungry you can hardly wait to eat. You would:
   a) put the food out on the table in its containers and go to it.
   b) take a little extra time and present the food in a way that makes it *look* nice, too.

8. When you remember your dreams do you remember:
   a) usually just the plot?
   b) the plot and the details of the setting?

SCORING:

	A	B
1.	0	5
2.	5	0
3.	0	5
4.	5	0
5.	0	5
6.	5	0
7.	0	5
8.	0	5

30–40: You are a visual person and probably have always been. You are aware of your surroundings, colors, and shapes. If you have not yet begun to develop your visual skills, you may want to start by taking photographs of things that are pleasing to your eye.

15–25: You may not have the talent to be a visual artist, but you are not oblivious to your surroundings. Sometimes to appreciate the way things look you have to remind yourself to *really* look at them.

0–10: Your sight is not your most developed sense. You can cultivate it, if you wish, by simply looking around you at times you otherwise would not.

Am I Verbal?

1. I write letters:
   a) only to people too far away to call.
   b) to friends and close relatives no matter where they live.

2. When I listen to a song on the radio, I:
   a) don't usually listen to the words but just to the music.
   b) like to listen to the words and sometimes memorize them, too.

3. I keep a diary:
   a) just to keep track of appointments.
   b) as a place to write down my ideas and feelings.

4. I read books:
   a) for school only.
   b) for school and for fun.

5. If I had to describe an unusual house to someone, I would:
   a) try to find the best words to describe it.
   b) draw a picture of it.

6. If I wanted to share a funny joke with friends but couldn't exactly remember how I heard it, I would:
   a) figure out a way to tell it in my own words.
   b) not tell it.

7. I find that I am often impressed with how articulate certain people are.
   a) rarely b) often

SCORING:

	A	B
1.	1	2
2.	1	2
3.	1	2
4.	1	2
5.	2	1
6.	2	1
7.	1	2

12–14: You are sensitive to language. You probably like to talk, read, write, and listen to other people. Simply, you like words in all their forms.

9–11: You're comfortable with language and enjoy its use in everyday life.

7–8: Language doesn't play a very important role in your life. While you may be stronger in other areas, you should try to master the use of language enough to enjoy the pleasures of communication.

Am I Mechanical?

1. Are you good at puzzles and do you enjoy figuring them out?
   a) not especially
   b) yes, definitely

2. In 2 minutes, how many uses could you think of for a rubberband?
   a) less than 9
   b) 10 or more

3. Which would be the easiest way for you to understand how a clock works?
   a) to take it apart and look at its inner workings.
   b) to read an explanation in a textbook.

4. When it comes to packing bags or loading cars, would you say you were:
   a) pretty good at it?
   b) not very good at it?

5. When things break, you
   a) throw them away or take them to a repair shop.
   b) try to fix them yourself.

SCORING:

	A	B
1.	0	5
2.	0	5
3.	5	0
4.	5	0
5.	0	5

15–25: You're mechanical. You like to work with your hands, take things apart, put them back together again, and figure out how they work.

0–10: You're not especially mechanical. That's okay, it just means you're talented in something else.

Am I Athletic?

1. Are you on any athletic teams by your own choice?
   Yes No

2. Have you been active in sports for as long as you can remember?
   Yes No

3. Are you active in more than 4 different sports?
   Yes No

4 Do you enjoy sports?
   Yes No

5. Do you find you quickly catch on to a new game?
   Yes No

6. Do you have endurance?
   Yes No

7. Would you say you are consistently improving at games you like best?
   Yes No

8. Are you coordinated?
   Yes No

9. Do you spend at least one third of your free time engaged in sports?
   Yes No

10. Would you feel something major was missing in your life if you didn't participate in sports?
    Yes No

SCORING:

6–10 yes answers: You're athletic and enjoy sports. Keep it up. It's great for the body and spirit.

0–5 yes answers: If you participate in sports at all, you probably aren't crazy about them. You don't have to compete, but it might make you feel surprisingly happy with yourself to find one sport you really like best and try to improve at it.

How Do I Deal with Family and Friends?

The way you act with particular people can say a lot about the way you are in general. You probably act very differently with your friends than you do with your family and still differently with people you don't know very well.

The fact that your personality seems to change from one situation to another doesn't mean you're strange, only that different people and different relationships bring out various sides of your personality. Stopping to think about these many sides of yourself can teach you a lot about the way you are. The way you deal with your mother and father, for example, even though that may change from one day to the next, is a good guide to how mature you are, how responsible, or how independent. Understanding your relationship with your brothers and sisters, on the other hand, can tell you something about how competitive you are and how playful. Friends bring out still other aspects. Your relationship with them can show you something about how loyal you are, how generous, or how concerned.

Think about the way you are with the various people you know. Now think about the way you are with people you don't know well. What do you think it says about you?

Parents?!?

As much as you may try to remember that your parents are people like everybody else, to you, your parents are the most important people in the world. Without them there would be no you, and growing up would be very difficult indeed. On the other hand, if you're like most teenagers, there are probably times when you feel your life would be much better without your parents around. That doesn't mean you don't love them. It just means that sometimes dealing with your parents can be very difficult. The relationship children have with their parents is a complicated and deep one. It can be terrible, wonderful, and then terrible again. What's your relationship with your parents? If you sometimes have problems, how much of the problem is your fault?

1. After you've had a disagreement with your parents, do you think you were right:
   a) most of the time?
   b) some of the time?
   c) almost never?

2. If your parents told you to baby-sit for your little sister and there was something else that you wanted to do, would you:
   a) feel angry but keep quiet and baby-sit anyway?
   b) storm out in a huff and refuse to baby-sit?
   c) try talking to them in the hope of working out a compromise?

3. When's the last time you thanked your parents for something nice they did for you?
   a) within the last few days.
   b) over a week ago.
   c) not for a long time.

4. When you talk to your parents about something that means a lot to you, you feel they:
   a) listen and care about what you're saying.
   b) aren't especially interested and don't listen to what you're saying.
   c) don't seem to understand what you're talking about.

5. If you come home from school unhappy, *your parents* would:
   a) probably not notice anything is wrong.
   b) press you to tell them what's bothering you.
   c) acknowledge that they notice something is wrong but not insist that you tell them what it is.

6. If you came home from school unhappy, *you* would:
   a) pretend nothing was the matter.
   b) talk to your parents about what was bothering you.
   c) sulk in your room and not talk to anyone.

SCORING:

	A	B	C
1.	5	15	10
2.	10	5	15
3.	15	10	5
4.	15	5	10
5.	5	10	15
6.	10	15	5

70–90 points means that in spite of a few problems, you and your parents seem to have a very good relationship. All of you seem to contribute to making it work. You understand that in order for it to keep working, you have to keep doing your share.

50–65 points means things are a little shaky now between you and your parents. Maybe if you put your pride aside and tried doing it their way for a while, you'd take some of the pressure off a sticky situation.

30–45 points means that as far as you're concerned, you're in a bad way with your mother and father right now. If it makes a difference to you, they're probably as upset about it as you are. But rest assured, it will get better. Adolescence is a hard time for parents as well as children.

Am I a Good Friend?

Being a good friend means many different things to many different people.

To some people it may mean you have the kind of patience that lets you listen to them tell the same story for the twelfth time without getting annoyed. Other people might think you're a good friend if you can make them laugh when they're feeling angry. Still others might call you a good friend if you leave them alone when they are feeling angry. But, most of all, being a good friend means being loyal to those you like very much, being reliable, being sensitive to your friends' needs, and, a lot of the time at least, being fun to be with. The success of a friendship, like most other important relationships, depends on give-and-take. Are you a good friend?

1. If a good friend invited me to go skating and I was happy sitting home watching TV, I would:
   a) say no and stay home.
   b) urge my friend to give up on the skating idea and come over and watch TV instead.
   c) go skating if my friend really wanted to go that badly.

2. The longest I've kept a friend is:
   a) 6 months to 1 year.
   b) 2 years.
   c) over 3 years.

3. If I had made advance plans to keep a good friend company while baby-sitting and then a person I had a crush on asked me out for the same night, I would:
   a) tell the date I was busy and take a rain check.
   b) make the date and hope my friend would understand.
   c) call up my friend, explain the situation, and, if I found my friend still wanted to see me, turn down the date.

4. When it comes to being confidential with my best friend:
   a) I never breathe a word of the secrets told me.
   b) there have been a few times when I let other people in on a secret told to me.
   c) we don't tell each other secrets.

5. When I argue with my best friend, even if I believe I am right I:
   a) can't cool down until my friend agrees with me.
   b) eventually give in or get off the subject rather than make a big deal.
   c) sooner or later begin to understand the other point of view.

SCORING:

	A	B	C
1.	5	10	15
2.	5	10	15
3.	15	5	10
4.	15	10	5
5.	5	10	15

A score of **55–75** points means you seem to be able to make and keep good friends. Because you appreciate the importance of friendship, you try especially hard to improve the relationships you have.

A score of **40–50** means you're not always as careful as you could be to maintain good feelings between you and your friends. Maybe you've been thinking a little too much about yourself lately. You care about your friends a lot. Do something today that will show it.

If you scored between **25–35**, chances are you haven't been the best of friends lately. A good friend will understand and forgive you as long as you make amends. Try being more generous and a little more fun to be with. You'll be amazed at the results.

How Do I Get Along with My Brother or Sister?

The relationship you have with your brother or sister is a very special one indeed. Aside from your mother and father, there is probably no one else in the world you feel so strongly about. But feeling strongly doesn't always mean feeling good. Just as there is probably no one you love as much as your brother or sister, there is probably no one you hate as much either. That's the trouble with brothers and sisters: one minute you can feel so good and silly with them and the next minute you can feel you want to kill them. Do you know your brother or sister? Do they know you? Have you ever stopped to think about why you feel the way you do about them?

1. Can you trust your brother or sister to keep a secret for you?
   Yes No

2. Do you think your brother or sister understands you?
   Yes No

3. If you felt that your brother or sister was up to no good would you tell him or her?
   Yes No

4. Does your brother or sister make an effort to get to know your friends?
   Yes No

5. Do you have private games or jokes just between you and your brother or sister?
   Yes No

6. Are you generous when it comes to sharing your belongings with your brother or sister?
   Yes No

7. Do you try to make up soon after a fight with your brother or sister?
   Yes No

8. Do you think your brother or sister is proud of you?
   Yes No

SCORING:

6–8 yes answers: If you've answered the questions honestly and you got this many yes answers, it means you've got a pretty good relationship with your brother or sister. Whatever you're both doing, it's right. Keep up the good work.

3–5 yes answers: Your relationship with your brother or sister could use some improving. Clearly you love them, but sometimes you may forget that they're people, too. Try reaching out and getting to know them on *their* terms. You might just find that they're not so creepy after all.

1–2 yes answers: No one needs to tell you, you've got a problem. Take some consolation though — you're not alone. Practically everyone's experienced rough times with a brother or sister at some point in their lives. Usually growing up takes care of a good deal of it. In the meantime, do your part and try suggesting that you do something together that you both like. You may also want to try apologizing first for a change. Good luck!

—V—

How Do I Act with the Opposite Sex?

These days one of the very few undisputable things that can be said about relationships between people of the opposite sex is that they are generally different from relationships between people of the same sex. Sometimes, different can be better and sometimes it can be worse. Different can be more uncomfortable, more exciting, more reckless, or just plain self-conscious. Mostly what different means will depend on the people involved. If you are an average teenager you are probably becoming acutely aware of what it means to you. The contrasts between you and teenagers of the opposite sex are maybe more apparent to you now than they ever were before.

You may be feeling different yourself. Have you ever felt your whole mood change when someone of the opposite sex enters a room? Have you ever heard yourself talking to a person of the opposite sex and known that you just didn't sound the same as when you talked to friends of your own sex? How many times have you looked back on a conversation with someone of the opposite sex and thought, "Wow, did I act like a jerk." Or maybe a conversation with someone of the opposite sex was the best conversation you can remember having had with anyone.

How do you feel in general about the opposite sex?

Am I Relaxed on a Date?

1. On a first date in a restaurant, do you often lose your appetite?
   Yes No

2. When your date talks, do you have trouble looking him or her straight in the eye?
   Yes No

3. Do you get embarrassed easily on a date?
   Yes No

4. Do you find yourself blushing more than usual?
   Yes No

5. Do you find you can't speak as easily when you're out on a date as you can normally?
   Yes No

6. Do you become uncoordinated on dates?
   Yes No

7. Do you sometimes have trouble concentrating on what you're talking about?
   Yes No

8. Do you feel fidgety when you're sitting close to your date?
   Yes No

9. Do you worry about most of the things you say to your date and think that they sound so dumb?
   Yes No

10. Do you find that you don't act like yourself on a date?
    Yes No

SCORING:

6–10 yes answers: Like most people you tend to be uncomfortable on a date (first dates especially!). Chances are your date is, too. Sometimes getting past the discomfort is as simple as acknowledging it.

0–5 yes answers: You've had your share of jitters on a date but you also know that they easily pass. Try to help your date relax a little, too.

Am I the Jealous Type?

1. If the third time out, your date begins to tell you about a previous person who had meant a lot to him or her, would you:
   a) instantly feel jealous no matter how long ago it was?
   b) be curious and interested in learning more about your date in the context of a previous relationship?

2. If you passed by the open door to the study hall and saw your special friend sitting alone at the same table with a member of the opposite sex, would you:
   a) walk by with not much more than a wince?
   b) try to get your special friend's attention and hope that the other person would notice, too?

3. If you overhear your special friend telling someone of the opposite sex a story you thought had been told only to you, would you:
   a) feel hurt and annoyed and say something about it?
   b) check out to see how the listener is reacting and take a certain amount of pride in feeling you may understand your special friend better than others do?

4. You are trying to reach your special friend on the phone and find the line busy for 20 minutes. You would:

a) feel upset and very anxious to know who your friend was talking to for that long.
b) get involved with something else and figure you'll call again a little bit later.

5. You are hoping to go to the movies on a Thursday with your special friend who, it turns out, is busy that night. You would:
a) accept that and try to make plans for another night.
b) insist on knowing why your friend is busy that night, what he or she is doing, and with whom.

SCORING:

	A	B
1.	5	0
2.	0	5
3.	5	0
4.	5	0
5.	0	5

15–25: There's no doubt about it, you know what it means to feel jealous. Unfortunately, your jealous feelings are so intense sometimes that it can be hard to know if there's any basis to them at all. Next time you get jealous try to think about the true source of the feeling. Is your friend really a flirt? Are you growing too dependent, or are you basically insecure? The best cure for jealousy is to understand it.

0–10: Few people could claim that they've never felt jealous and that goes for you, too. You do, however, seem to have your jealousy under control and that's good.

Am I as Considerate as Possible?

1. Do I make a special point of looking my best when going out on a date?
   Yes No

2. Am I ready on time for most dates?
   Yes No

3. If I have to cancel a date do I give enough notice?
   Yes No

4. Do I make an effort not to monopolize conversations?
   Yes No

5. Do I really listen when my date talks?
   Yes No

6. Am I polite?
   Yes No

7. Am I considerate?
   Yes No

8. Am I fun to be with?
   Yes No

9. Am I flexible?
   Yes No

10. Am I clear about what I like and don't like?
    Yes No

11. Am I clear about what I will and will not do?
    Yes No

12. Do I avoid hurting other people's feelings?
    Yes No

13. Do I keep up my half of the conversation?
    Yes No

14. Do I know how to show an interest in someone?
    Yes No

15. Do I have a sense of humor?
    Yes No

SCORING:

1–5 yes answers: You've got some work to do. Your "considerate" quotient is way down. If you're not getting the results you want with the opposite sex, this could be the reason. Being considerate, fun, and sensitive is the stuff of romance. Try it!

6–10 yes answers: You're straddling the fence considerate-wise. Get your act together and give it your all. You'll feel better and have more fun, too.

11–15 yes answers: You understand the importance of being as considerate as possible even though you slip up every once in a while. Keep up the good work; it's worth it!

VI

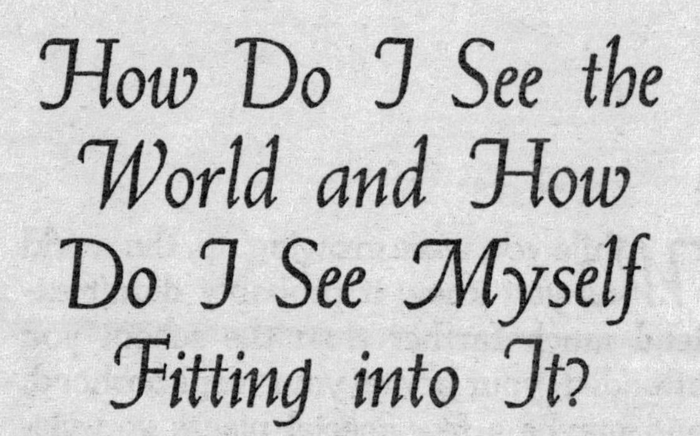

While you were growing up, the world as you knew it probably didn't extend much farther than the school you attended, your home, your neighborhood, and maybe a few special places you visited with family or friends.

Now that you're getting older, maybe you've traveled or read enough about other places to know that your town is just one small part of the world and an even smaller part of the whole universe.

You've also probably noticed that not everybody all over the world lives the same way you do. Life in the country is different from life in the city, and people dress differently, speak differently, and generally enjoy different styles of living in different parts of the world.

Maybe you've wondered about where and how you'll live when you grow up. Do you want to stay in your hometown or in another town like it, or do you want to move far away to a place unlike anything you've known and experienced? Do you want to live in the country, close to nature and far away from crowds, or do you want to live a faster life in a large, busy city?

Do I Keep Well Informed of Current Events?

1. Do you know the names of the 3 top government officials in your town?
   Yes No

2. Though you may not be of voting age, did you follow the last presidential campaign and did you know who you would have voted for?
   Yes No

3. Do you read the newspaper?
   Yes No

4. Do you watch the news?
   Yes No

5. Would you be able to identify the areas in the world currently in crisis?
   Yes No

6. Do you know which countries are presently at war, if any are?
   Yes No

7. Do you know where in the world there have been natural disasters in the last year?
   Yes No

8. Do you know the names of the major world leaders?
   Yes No

9. Do you understand the effect of food and energy consumption on world politics?
   Yes No

10. Do you understand the electoral process?
    Yes No

SCORING:

1–5 yes answers: With so much going on, and so fast, it's sometimes hard to keep up with current events. You've got some catching up to do. Watch the news every night for a week and you'll be on your way.

6–10 yes answers: Good for you! You seem to be keeping track of what's going on in the world. You know and appreciate that before you can formulate your own opinions you have to know the facts.

Do I Have a Sense of Community Responsibility?

1. If there were a drive in my town to collect clothing for children less fortunate than myself, I would:
   a) probably not know about it.
   b) do the best I could to appeal to family and friends to donate whatever clothing they could afford to give.
   c) help out in the drive and donate some of my own clothes as well.

2. If while I was walking home from school I unwrapped a candy bar and found there was no trash can nearby and nobody watching me, I would:

a) drop the wrapper on the street and keep walking.
b) stuff the wrapper in my pocket and hold on to it until I found a trash can.
c) drop the wrapper and kick it in the gutter.

3. If I were to find a stack of library books behind the town baseball field, I would:
   a) look through it and take home any that appealed to me.
   b) leave them there.
   c) pick them up and return them to the library.

4. If I were standing with a group of kids outside our school building and someone took out a can of spray paint to write on the school walls, I would:
   a) try to discourage the person from doing it.
   b) walk away from the crowd.
   c) stick around and be on the lookout for school authorities.

SCORING:

	A	B	C
1.	5	10	15
2.	5	15	10
3.	5	10	15
4.	15	10	5

20–40: You're becoming aware of yourself within the context of your community, but you're not always the most responsible. When there's a lot going on inside your head it's sometimes hard to remember the needs of others. Don't forget that it can be satisfying to give as well as to get.

45–60: You appreciate how important the role of the individual is within the community and you're doing your part. You understand that crime control, cleanliness, effective services, and community spirit all depend on individuals taking their share of responsibility. Try getting your friends in on your campaign for a better town. You'll all benefit from it.

Can I Change the World?

1. I believe elections are:
   a) pointless and don't really make a difference.
   b) an important way that individuals can influence government.

2. When I grow up I want to do something that:
   a) improves the quality of somebody's life besides myself.
   b) will make me rich and happy.

3. I want to have children because:
   a) that's the way it's supposed to be, and besides, I like children.
   b) I want to be a good parent and pass on good feelings to another generation.

4. Political problems make me feel:
   a) angry and determined to try to do something to effect a change.
   b) depressed and as if nothing I could do would ever make a difference.

5. When I think about growing up I often think about:
   a) what I want to do.
   b) what I want to have.

SCORING:

	A	B
1.	0	5
2.	5	0
3.	0	5
4.	5	0
5.	5	0

0–15: You're only beginning to think of yourself as someone who could have an influence on society. You probably feel that your hands are full just thinking about yourself. Once you begin to figure out what you can offer the world, you can start to make your own personal contributions.

20–25: You're learning that it's not necessary to be a genius to contribute to the world in a positive way. Changing the world has more to do with attitude than achievement and you've got the right attitude.

Where in the World Will I Live?

1. When I go for a walk I:
   a) enjoy bumping into people I know and greeting others I recognize but don't know as well.
   b) like to be left alone to enjoy my privacy.

2. Crowds make me feel:
   a) excited.
   b) nervous.

3. I would prefer to live in a place where:
   a) there's always a lot going on and things to do that I've never done before.
   b) there isn't an overwhelming amount of social activities to choose from.

4. My social life:
   a) is not such an important part of my life.
   b) is something I wouldn't want to live without.

5. Fresh air, trees, flowers, and open spaces are:
   a) nice for a vacation.
   b) the kinds of things I want surrounding me in my everyday life.

6. When I go shopping I:
   a) go to stores where I am known.
   b) don't like to dawdle but just want to get my shopping done and go.

7. Given the choice between two equally spacious homes, I would rather live:
   a) in an apartment.
   b) in a house.

8. When I do finally decide where to live and get my own place, I figure it will be:
   a) someplace where I can settle down and remain as long as possible.
   b) a temporary arrangement. I can't see staying in any one place for too long.

9. I would rather live someplace where:
   a) I am around people with similar backgrounds to my own.

b) I'm around a mixture of people from different places and of different backgrounds.

10. I find the quiet of the country
    a) very peaceful.
    b) creepy.

SCORING:

	A	B
1.	5	0
2.	0	5
3.	0	5
4.	5	0
5.	0	5
6.	5	0
7.	0	5
8.	5	0
9.	5	0
10.	5	0

25–50: Right now, you seem to be partial to life in a small town and to all the comforts that come with it. You like feeling a sense of belonging in your community and knowing and being known by the people around you. Open spaces mean a lot to you. So does feeling established in one place.

0–20: City life seems to be your preference. You like the feeling of many things going on nearby, and you enjoy having many people around you. A fast-paced life excites you, as does the possibility of meeting new and different people and trying things you've never done before.

What in the World Will I Do?

1. I think I would be happiest working:
   a) in a large office with lots of people.
   b) in the comfort of my home.
   c) outdoors.

2. When I get the kind of job I want, I will probably be spending most of my time:
   a) at meetings with people.
   b) at my desk alone.
   c) in a private office or studio.

3. I'll probably be:
   a) talking a lot.
   b) working with my hands a lot.
   c) reading and writing a lot.

4. A successful career means to me:
   a) making lots of money.
   b) becoming very good at my craft.
   c) being in a powerful position.

5. Of the following 3 categories, my job will fall under:
   a) Service.
   b) The Arts.
   c) Business.

SCORING:

	A	B	C
1.	30	10	20
2.	30	20	10
3.	20	10	30
4.	30	10	20
5.	20	10	30

50–80: You see yourself working in small, relatively quiet settings. That could mean in a small office, working closely with a few people, or even alone if your work calls for that. For now, at least, you visualize yourself doing the kind of work that's creative and concentrated.

90–110: You obviously like people and therefore can easily imagine yourself working well with them. You prefer situations where you can work on a one-to-one basis with another person either as a partner or in a helping capacity.

120–150: You can imagine yourself working in a large corporation or office and enjoying the stimulation of responsibility and competition. You like the idea of important business operations going on around you, and knowing that you can participate in at least some part of their development is very appealing to you.